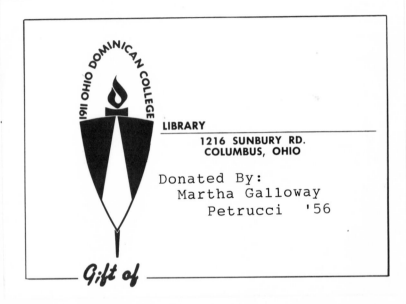

THE COMIC
ADVENTURES OF
OLD MOTHER HUBBARD
AND HER
DOG

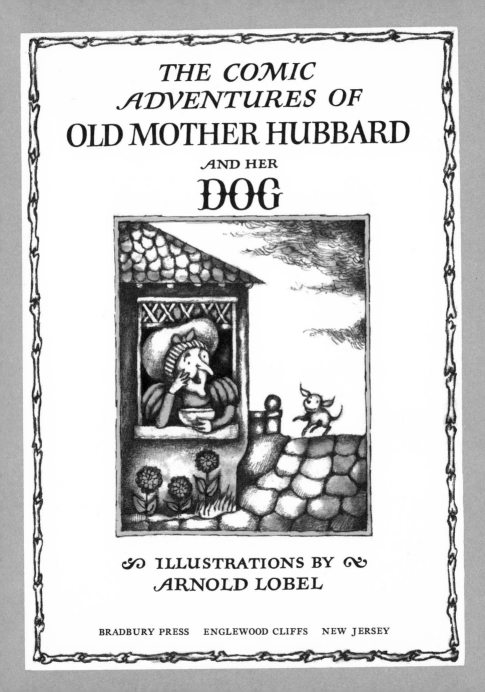

∽ ILLUSTRATIONS BY ∾
ARNOLD LOBEL

BRADBURY PRESS   ENGLEWOOD CLIFFS   NEW JERSEY

FOR JULIAN
AND BENJAMIN
AND TOM
AND VIRGINIA

Old Mother Hubbard
Went to the cupboard,
To fetch her poor dog a bone;

But when she got there
The cupboard was bare
And so the poor dog had none.

She went to the baker's
  To buy him some bread;

But when she came back
The poor dog was dead.

She went to the undertaker's
To buy him a coffin;

But when she came back
	The poor dog was laughing.

She took a clean dish
  To get him some tripe;

But when she came back
He was smoking a pipe.

She went to the fishmonger's
To buy him some fish;

But when she came back
He was licking the dish.

She went to the tavern
  For white wine and red;

But when she came back
　　The dog stood on his head.

She went to the fruiterer's
To buy him some fruit;

But when she came back
    He was playing the flute.

She went to the tailor's
  To buy him a coat;

But when she came back
He was riding a goat.

She went to the hatter's
To buy him a hat;

But when she came back
He was feeding the cat.

She went to the barber's
To buy him a wig;

But when she came back
He was doing the jig.

She went to the cobbler's
　　To buy him some shoes;

But when she came back
   He was reading the news.

She went to the seamstress
    To buy him some linen;

But when she came back
The dog was a-spinning.

She went to the hosier's
  To buy him some hose;

But when she came back
　　He was dressed in his clothes.

The dame made a curtsey,
The dog made a bow;

The dame said, Your servant,
The dog said, Bow-wow.

THE END